Lovable Dogs

COLORING BOOK

Brenda Abdoyan

DESIGN ORIGINALS
an Imprint of Fox Chapel Publishing
www.d-originals.com

D1401931

BASIC TOOLS FOR ADDING COLOR

Coloring, luckily, offers many options for how to apply your hues. Here you can see the same dog face colored three different times. Each dog was colored using a different coloring tool. Method #1 was colored with permanent markers; method #2 was colored using colored pencils and watercolor pencils combined (following the manufacturer's instructions); and, finally, method #3 was colored using basic watercolor paint. Not only are your color schemes unlimited (as you can see on the next page), but you also have a lot of tools at your disposal. It's totally up to you to decide what you like best.

Method #1:
Permanent Markers

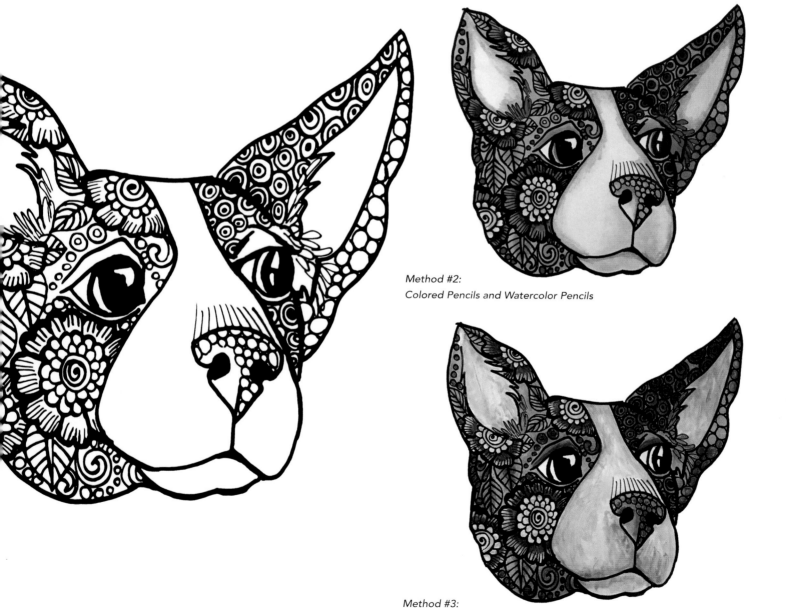

Method #2:
Colored Pencils and Watercolor Pencils

Method #3:
Watercolor Paint

Basic Coloring Options

Coloring an image is like bringing to life. The best part of having the ability to give life to a drawn image is that there is no limit to what you can do! You can decide how your version of the image will look. Anything goes; whatever you can imagine, you can color.

In my colored examples, I used the same original dog drawing with a few color variations. However, not only did I add color, I also left some spaces completely without color. Then I decided to add more details to the eyes (with thin black accent lines), and add eyebrows and varying whiskers!

Relax and have fun! That is the only rule in your world full of color.

Decorative color scheme

Natural color scheme

Cool color scheme

Pop art color scheme

I had so much fun coloring my own designs that I had to stop myself before I went and colored the whole book! But what is also fun is seeing how other artists color my work. On the following pages, check out how color brought these dogs to life. We used various different mediums, so you're sure to find some inspiration for your own coloring, no matter what medium you're using. Enjoy the vibrant examples on these pages, and then get coloring yourself!

Markers (Sharpie, Tombow, Letraset ProMarkers, Bic). Color by Brenda Abdoyan.

Colored pencils, markers. Color by Darla Tjelmeland.

Markers (Sharpie, Tombow, Letraset ProMarkers, Bic). Color by Brenda Abdoyan.

Markers (Sharpie, Tombow, Letraset ProMarkers, Bic).
Color by Brenda Abdoyan.

Watercolor pencils. Color by Darla Tjelmeland.

Markers (Sharpie, Tombow, Letraset ProMarkers, Bic).
Color by Brenda Abdoyan.

Markers (Sharpie, Tombow, Letraset ProMarkers, Bic).
Color by Brenda Abdoyan.

Markers (Prismacolor). Color by Darla Tjelmeland.

Markers (Sharpie, Tombow, Letraset ProMarkers, Bic). Color by Brenda Abdoyan.

Markers. Color by Darla Tjelmeland.

Markers (Sharpie, Tombow, Letraset ProMarkers, Bic). Color by Brenda Abdoyan.

Watercolor pencils. Color by Darla Tjelmeland.

Markers (Sharpie, Tombow, Letraset ProMarkers, Bic). Color by Brenda Abdoyan.

Markers (Sharpie, Tombow, Letraset ProMarkers, Bic). Color by Brenda Abdoyan.

Markers (Sharpie, Tombow, Letraset ProMarkers, Bic). Color by Brenda Abdoyan.

Markers (Sharpie, Tombow, Letraset ProMarkers, Bic). Color by Brenda Abdoyan.

Colored pencils (Prismacolor). Color by Darla Tjelmeland.

Watercolor pencils. Color by Darla Tjelmeland.

Markers (Sharpie, Bic). Color by Darla Tjelmeland.

Markers (Sharpie, Tombow, Letraset ProMarkers, Bic).
Color by Brenda Abdoyan.

Markers (Sharpie, Tombow, Letraset ProMarkers, Bic).
Color by Brenda Abdoyan.

You can usually tell that a man is good
if he has a dog who loves him.

—W. BRUCE CAMERON, *A DOG'S JOURNEY*

Abby

Dogs are not our whole life,
but they make our lives whole.

—ROGER A. CARAS

Alexi

If a dog will not come to you
after having looked you in the face,
you should go home
and examine your conscience.

—WOODROW WILSON

Once you have had a wonderful dog,
a life without one is a life diminished.

—DEAN KOONTZ, *A BIG LITTLE LIFE: A MEMOIR OF A
JOYFUL DOG NAMED TRIXIE*

Bessie Basset

© Brenda Abdoyan, www.bajidoo.com

Acquiring a dog may be the only time
a person gets to choose a relative.

—Mordecai Siegal

Bianca Wolf

I'm suspicious of people who don't
like dogs, but I trust a dog when
it doesn't like a person.

—UNKNOWN

_____
_____
_____
_____
_____
_____
_____
_____
_____

Brigget's Walk

Whoever said you can't buy
happiness forgot little puppies.

—GENE HILL

_____
_____
_____
_____
_____
_____
_____
_____
_____
_____

Buster

If you think dogs can't count, try
putting three dog biscuits in your
pocket and then giving him
only two of them.

—PHIL PASTORET

_____
_____
_____
_____
_____
_____
_____
_____
_____
_____
_____

Charo

If I could be half the person my dog is,
I'd be twice the human I am.

—CHARLES YU

_____
_____
_____
_____
_____
_____
_____
_____

Chevi

A dog is the only thing on Earth that
loves you more than he loves himself.

—Josh Billings

Dolly

I've seen a look in dogs' eyes,
a quickly vanishing look of amazed
contempt, and I am convinced that
basically dogs think humans are nuts.

—JOHN STEINBECK

You can say any foolish thing
to a dog, and the dog will give you
a look that says, "Wow, you're right!
I never would've thought of that!"

—DAVE BARRY

Echo in the Grass

© Brenda Abdoyan, www.bajidoo.com

The great pleasure of a dog is that
you may make a fool of yourself with
him and not only will he not scold you,
but he will make a fool of himself too.

—SAMUEL BUTLER

© Brenda Abdoyan, www.bajidoo.com

The world would be a nicer place if
everyone had the ability to love
as unconditionally as a dog.

—M.K. CLINTON, *SHOWSTOPPERS*

Frenchy

I once decided not to date a guy because he wasn't excited to meet my dog. I mean, this was like not wanting to meet my mother.

—BONNIE SCHACHTER

Jennifer

Things that upset a terrier may pass
virtually unnoticed by a Great Dane.

—Smiley Blanton

The only creatures that are evolved
enough to convey pure love
are dogs and infants.

—JOHNNY DEPP

Kaytie

© Brenda Abdoyan, www.bajidoo.com

No one appreciates the very special
genius of your conversation
as the dog does.

—CHRISTOPHER MORLEY

Lucile

There is no psychiatrist in the world
like a puppy licking your face.
—BEN WILLIAMS

Lucy

Anybody who doesn't know what
soap tastes like never washed a dog.

—FRANKLIN P. JONES

Merlin

© Brenda Abdoyan, www.bajidoo.com

If there are no dogs in Heaven,
then when I die I want to go
where they went.

—WILL ROGERS

_____
_____
_____
_____
_____
_____
_____
_____

Minni

A dog can express more with his
tail in minutes than his owner can
express with his tongue in hours.

—Unknown

NuNu

When an eighty-five pound mammal
licks your tears away, then tries to sit
on your lap, it's hard to feel sad.

—KRISTAN HIGGINS

What does a dog do on his day off?
He can't lie around—that's his job.

—GEORGE CARLIN

The most affectionate creature
in the world is a wet dog.

—AMBROSE BIERCE

_____
_____
_____
_____
_____
_____
_____
_____
_____
_____

Ruby Resting

© Brenda Abdoyan, www.bajidoo.com

A dog is one of the remaining reasons
why some people can be persuaded
to go for a walk.

—O.A. BATTISTA

Ruby

© Brenda Abdoyan, www.bajidoo.com

Dogs do speak, but only to those
who know how to listen.

—ORHAN PAMUK

Sara in the Grass

I think dogs are the most
amazing creatures;
they give unconditional love.
For me, they are the role model
for being alive.

—GILDA RADNER

_____
_____
_____
_____
_____
_____
_____
_____
_____

© Brenda Abdoyan, www.bajidoo.com

Don't accept your dog's admiration
as conclusive evidence
that you are wonderful.

—ANN LANDERS

_____
_____
_____
_____
_____
_____
_____
_____
_____

Yello Dog

© Brenda Abdoyan, www.bajidoo.com

I have found that when you are
deeply troubled, there are things
you get from the silent devoted
companionship of a dog that you can
get from no other source.

—DORIS DAY

Yorkie Boy